USED EXTENSIVELY IN NURSERY SCHOOLS

Foundation Nursery Sounds Book 1

Schofield & Sims

NURSERY SOUNDS 1

Name

Scamp says **b** as in **b**at.

Can you say '**b**'?
Now say the words for the pictures and listen to the **b**eginning sound.

Write **b**

b b b b b b

Say **b b b b b**

Colour the pictures **b**eginning with the sound **b**.

Draw **B**enjamin **B**ear.

Say "**B**enjamin **B**ear **b**ounces **b**ig **b**alls."

Can you think of more things **b**eginning with the '**b**' sound?

Scamp says c as in coat.

Can you say 'c'?
Who is chasing Scamp?
Say the words and listen
to the beginning sound.

Write c

Say c c c c c

Draw the **c**astle. Scamp is going to the **c**astle. **C**olour the things beginning with the sound '**c**' that have fallen from Scamp's **c**ase.

Say "**C**assandra **c**uddles the **c**ute **c**at."

5

Scamp says **d** as in **d**ot.

Can you say '**d**'?

Scamp is having a **d**onkey ride. What things can he see that begin with '**d**'? Say the words and listen to the beginning sound.

Write **d**

d d d d d d d

6

Say **d d d d d**

Scamp has opened the **d**oor.
Colour all the things that begin with the sound '**d**'.

Draw **d**iplodocus **d**inosaur.

Say "**D**ippy **D**inosaur **d**ances **d**aily with **D**aisy **D**olly."

Can you think of more words beginning with the '**d**' sound?

Scamp says **f** as in **f**an.

Can you say '**f**'? What can you see in the picture that begins with the sound '**f**'? Say the words and listen to the beginning sound.

Write **f**

8

Say f f f f f

What can Scamp see hidden in the **f**orest?
Colour all the things beginning with the sound '**f**'.

Draw a **f**ish and its **f**in.

Say "**F**our **f**unny **f**ish **f**ind **f**ive **f**ancy **f**eathers."

Can you think of other words that begin
with the '**f**' sound?

9

Scamp sings **g** as in **g**ate.

Can you say '**g**'?

Who can hear Scamp singing? Say the words and listen to the beginning sound.

Who is **g**alloping away?

Write **g**

Say g g g g g

Colour all the things in Scamp's **g**arden that have the beginning sound '**g**'.

Say "**G**olden **g**oose **g**ave **g**oldfish to **g**iggling **g**irls."

Draw the **g**uard outside the **g**ate.

Scamp says **h** as in **h**at.
Can you say '**h**'?
Hold your **h**and in front of your mouth and say **h h h h**.
Can you feel it?
Now say these words and listen to the beginning sound.

Write **h**

Say **h h h h h**

What has the **h**owling **h**urricane blown into Scamp's **h**ouse?

What else can you see beginning with the '**h**' sound?

Draw a **h**edgehog.

Say "**H**enrietta **H**en **h**ides **h**er **h**orseshoes from **h**edgehogs."

Scamp says **j** as in jam.

Can you say 'j'?
What can Scamp see beginning with the 'j' sound?
Say the words and listen to the beginning sound.

Write **j**

Say **j j j j**

Scamp is driving his **j**eep in the **j**ungle. Help him find a **j**aguar, a **j**elly, a **j**ackdaw and a **j**acket. Colour them red.

Draw the **j**uggler.

Say "**J**umping **J**ester **J**im **j**uggles **j**unk."

Can you **j**ive, **j**og and **j**iggle?

Scamp says **k** as in **k**ey.
Can you say '**k**'?
Now say these words and
listen to the beginning sound.

Write **k**

k k k k k k

16

Say k k k k k

Where is Scamp? Finish the picture.
Colour the things Scamp can see beginning with the sound 'k'.

Say "Kind kitten kicks a kipper."

Give each animal a name beginning with the sound 'k'.

Scamp says **l** as in **l**ips.

Can you say 'l'?
What is Scamp reading?
Now say these words and
listen for the beginning sound.

Write **l**

Say l l l l l

Help Scamp to load his lorry with things beginning with the 'l' sound. Draw a line from the picture to the lorry.

Draw **Larry lamb**.

Say "Little lazy Larry lamb likes licking lollipops."

Can you think of more words beginning with the 'l' sound?

Scamp says **m** as in **m**at.

Can you say '**m**'?

Now say these words and listen to the beginning sound.

Draw the **m**an in the **m**oon.

Write **m**

m m m m m m m

20

Say m m m m m

Scamp is on a **m**ountain. Join all the things beginning with the sound '**m**' to the **m**ountain.

Say "**M**ad **m**onster **m**ops up **m**ilky **m**ess!"

The **m**onster's name begins with the sound '**m**'.
Give the **m**onster a name beginning with the sound '**m**'.

Scamp says **n** as in **n**et.

Can you say '**n**'?

What is Scamp reading? Say these words and listen to the beginning sound.

Write **n**

Say **n n n n n**

Here are Scamp's **n**utty **n**eighbours **N**orman and **N**ellie. Draw **N**orman's **n**eck and **n**ose. Draw **N**ellie.

Say "**N**aughty **N**orman needs **N**ellie's **n**ecklace."

Schofield & Sims
HELPING CHILDREN TO LEARN

Schofield & Sims was established in 1901 by two headmasters and since then our name has been synonymous with educationally sound texts and teaching materials. Our mission is to publish products which are:

- **Educationally sound** • **Good value** • **Written by experienced teachers**
- **Extensively used in schools, nurseries and play groups**
- **Used by parents to support their children's learning**

NURSERY SOUNDS BOOK 1

A series of six books introducing the early stages of phonics through fun activities which are carefully structured to stimulate conversation, increase vocabulary and encourage knowledge and use of early word building.

Nursery Sounds Book 1 - 0 7217 0855 2

Nursery Sounds Book 2 - 0 7217 0856 0

Nursery Sounds Book 3 - 0 7217 0857 9

Nursery Sounds Book 4 - 0 7217 0858 7

Nursery Sounds Book 5 - 0 7217 0925 7

Nursery Sounds Book 6 - 0 7217 0926 5

Schofield & Sims pre-school products for 4+ year olds

Posters
Sturdy, laminated posters, full colour, write-on/wipe-off, suitable for wall mounting or desk top use. Over 70 titles including the alphabet, numbers, colours, days, shapes, nursery rhymes, opposites, seasons, time, weather and our bodies.

Nursery workbooks
Nursery Numbers
Books 1 - 6
A series of six wook books which comprise a carefully structured programme of early number work giving children a sound understanding of numbers, number patterns, money, measurement and basic mathematical vocabulary in preparation for Key Stage1.

Nursery All About
Books 1 - 4
Series consists of four books: All About Me, All About Where I Live, All About The World I Live In and All About The Weather. Each book is designed to develop young children's awareness of their environment, helping to sharpen their powers of observation and consolidate basic concepts and skills. Enthusiasm for learning is encouraged through fun activities, which give ample opportunity for parental support.

Nursery Land
Books 1 - 4
A brand new series of workbooks packed with activities based on popular nursery rhymes, to help develop basic concepts and skills. Includes dot-to-dot, numbers 1-10, colour, shape, size, matching and odd one out.

Nursery Writing
Books 1 - 6
A series of graded workbooks to aid the development of pre-reading and early writing skills, including left-to-right co-ordination, pencil control, visual perception, letter recognition, the alphabet, word recognition, and word writing. Fun-to-do exercises reinforce and develop skills and understanding.

Nursery Activity
Books 1 - 6
This graded series of six activity books helps pre-school children apply their practical and oral skills to more concrete written work. Exercises cover a variety of pre-reading and early mathematical skills to help development of left and right co-ordination, sequencing, counting and number writing practice, shape and number recognition and colour recognition.

Information
For further information about products for pre-school, Key Stage 1 and 2, please request our catalogue or visit our website at

www.schofieldandsims.co.uk

Schofield & Sims

Dogley Mill, Fenay Bridge, Huddersfield, HD8 0NQ
Phone 01484 607080   Fax 01484 606815

e-mail sales@schofieldandsims.co.uk

Author   Sally Johnson
Illustrator   Linzi Henry

©2001 Schofield & Sims Ltd.

All rights reserved. No part of this publication may be recorded or transmitted in any form or by any means or stored in any information storage or retrieval system without written permission of the copyright owner or in accordance with the Copyright Designs and Patents Act 1988. The doing of an unauthorised act in relation to a copyright work may result in both a civil claim for damages and criminal prosecution.

Warning
*These publications are **not** part of the copyright licensing scheme run by the Copyright Licensing Agency and may not be photocopied or mechanically copied in any other way, without written permission from the publisher.*

First printed 2001
Reprinted 2002, 2004

Printed by Fulcrum Colour Printers, Ripponden

ISBN 0-7217-0855-2

9 780721 708553

Price £1.95
Pre-School
Age Range 4+ years